CW00391597

A Viking Raid

It is a bright sunny day. Some of the Viking men are preparing to go on a voyage to see if they can find new supplies as their stocks of food are running low.

Eric's father, Harald, is a brave and fearsome fighter who is loyal to his friends.

Astrid, Eric's mother, is worried about how she is going to feed the family through the coming winter.

A Viking boat is being loaded with supplies for a voyage

The boat is very strong and will carry them safely through storms at sea.

The boy's name is Eric. This is the first time he has been on a voyage. He is a little frightened but very proud. Eric has two brothers and two sisters.

Glossary

voyage *a long sea journey*
fearsome *frightening*

Getting it right

Choose the right phrases to complete these sentences.

1 The setting is in a village (close to the sea.) (on the hillside.)

2 The main characters are (Eric and his friends.) (Eric and his family.)

3 The men are getting the Viking boat ready (for a long voyage.) (for a short fishing trip.)

4 Eric is excited because he is (going on his first voyage.) (staying in the village with Astrid.)

The start of the story

Write a sentence to answer these questions:

1 What is the name of Eric's father?

2 Name two activities that are going on in the picture as they get ready for the voyage.

3 How does Eric feel about the voyage?

4 What is Eric's mother worried about?

5 Why are the men setting out on a voyage?

Comprehension

- To find detailed information about the beginnings of stories

Helpful words

supplies winter Harald
family frightened
mending loading
boat food proud

Writing

- To plan a story, identifying different stages

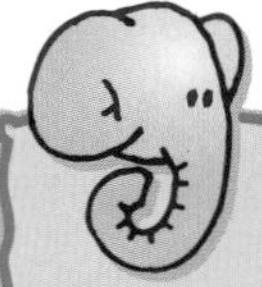

Remember

To make notes you need to write down **key words** and **phrases** about the Viking raid.

Ideas for the story

1 Look at this picture and write some short notes about what is happening.
Like this:

Vikings are stealing food.

Now write some more notes yourself.

2 This is the last picture about the story.
Write some notes about what you can see.
Like this:

boat has been damaged

Now write some more notes yourself.

Planning the story

Draw this table in your book.
Use the pictures above and writing you have done to help you fill in the information about scene 2 and scene 3.

	Setting	Characters	Action
Scene 1	A village by the sea, on a boat.	Eric, Harald, his father Astrid, his mother Eric's brothers and sisters	boat being loaded Eric helping
Scene 2			

Two Lists

I'm going out now
To the shops for my dad

I've got two lists
One of things to buy

Carrots
Peas
Bread
An apple-pie

One of things to remember:

Don't talk to strangers
Go straight home
Be careful crossing the roads
Don't talk to strangers
Come straight back
Don't lose the money
Don't talk to strangers
Don't get lost
Don't forget the change

And Tommy…

Yes, Dad?

Don't talk to strangers

I'm back now from going
To the shops for my dad

I didn't talk to strangers
I went straight there
I was careful crossing the roads
I didn't talk to strangers
I came straight back
I didn't lose the money
I didn't talk to strangers
I didn't get lost
I didn't forget the change
And … I didn't talk to strangers

So what did you forget?
Dad said

The carrots
The peas
The apple-pie
And…

Yes?

The bread

Tony Bradman

Comprehension

- To think carefully about the detailed content of a poem

Helpful words

carrots remember
bread apple-pie
buy things
peas talk

Remember

Don't forget to use capital letters and full stops.

What can you remember?

1 Where was Tommy going?

2 Who asked Tommy to do the shopping?

3 What did Tommy have to buy?

4 What were the two lists about?

5 What did Tommy have to remember about strangers?

6 What had Tommy forgotten when he arrived back home?

Is it true?

Copy these sentences into your book.

Write *true*, *false* or *can't tell* next to each one.

1 *Tommy went straight to the shops.*

2 *Tommy bought some sweets.*

3 *Tommy lost his money.*

4 *Tommy was shopping for his mum.*

5 *It was a sunny day when Tommy went shopping.*

6 *Tommy had to cross the road to get to the shops.*

Making lists

1 Tommy is writing his first list.
Copy and finish it.

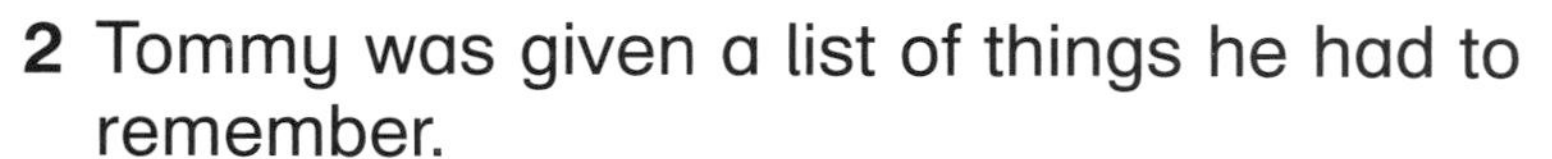

Writing

- To organise and write lists

2 Tommy was given a list of things he had to remember.
Look at them carefully.
Write them in order of importance.
Start with what you think is the most important.
Don't forget to number them.

Tip
Be careful! Some of the instructions are repeated.

Tommy's day

Tommy has a very busy day on Tuesday. Look at all the things he must do. Plan the day for Tommy. Show him the best order to do everything.

Use the headings:

Morning	Afternoon

Make bullet points under each one.

Tip
Go to the library to change my library book
can be shortened to:
- *change library book*

THE DAY THE ROOF FELL IN

From our special reporter: James Matthews

THE FIRE AND RESCUE SERVICES ARRIVED quickly on the scene at Nuffield Primary School yesterday when part of the flat roof suddenly caved in.

Over fifty children were working in the two rooms when, without any warning, a large section of the roof unexpectedly collapsed under the weight of hundreds of litres of water. "The rainwater must have been unable to escape due to a nest we found in the drainpipe," said the chief officer.

The children were all unharmed. Indeed they seemed to think it was all great fun, but they had to go home early as most were soaked to the skin. "Just think," said Annie Desai, "that little bird gave us all a holiday, and just when we were starting a maths lesson!"

The headmaster, Mr Morris, said that it was a miracle no one had been hurt.

The school will remain closed until next Monday, while emergency repairs are done to the roof.

Comprehension

- To tell the difference between fact and opinion

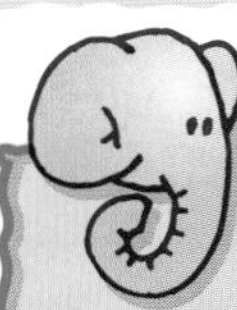

Remember

Questions must finish with a **?**

Asking questions

These are the kinds of question a reporter might ask when reporting on this incident.

Match the notes he made to the questions he asked.

1 *What is the name of the school where the roof collapsed?*

2 *How many children were working in the rooms that were flooded?*

3 *What caused the collapse of the roof?*

4 *Were any of the children hurt?*

5 *What will happen next?*

None of the children were hurt.

A nest was blocking the drainpipe so that the water could not escape.

School to remain closed until next Monday, while emergency repairs are done.

Nuffield Primary School.

More than fifty children

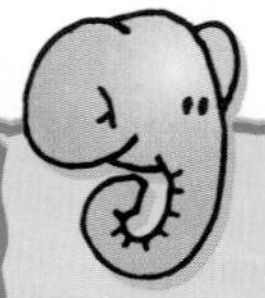

Remember

A **fact** is something that definitely happened.

An **opinion** is something that someone thinks.

Fact or opinion?

Copy these sentences.

Next to each write *fact* or *opinion*.

Part of the roof of the school collapsed.

All the children were very happy that they didn't need to go to school until Monday.

A nest was found in the drainpipe.

Without the Fire and Rescue Services things would have been much worse.

The children seemed to think it had all been great fun!

Writing

- To write and edit a newspaper article

Making it shorter

You have been asked to rewrite the article about the roof collapse for a national newspaper but there is only a small space available.

Without looking back at the article on page 10, try to write it using no more than fifty words.

Draft it first on scrap paper so that you can cross out and improve things if you need to.

Think of a new headline for your article.

Now write it neatly in your book.

Helpful words

Nuffield Primary School
Fire and Rescue Services
collapsed blocked
rainwater closed
emergency repairs

Become a reporter

Think of something that has happened at your school and write an article about it. It might be about a visit or a special event or concert.

Start a new paragraph for each new section in your article.

You only have a limited space so make sure that the most important information is included.

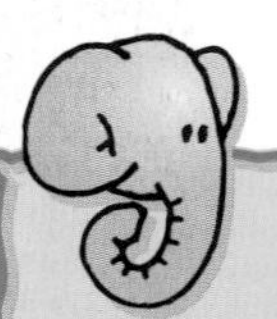

Remember

A **paragraph** is a group of sentences about the same thing.

Start each paragraph on a new line.

Fetch the Slipper

Grandad came downstairs one morning looking very cross and grumpy.

He looked as grumpy as a giraffe with a sore throat.

"I've lost one of my slippers," he grumbled. "One of my best red velvet slippers, that Betty sent from America. Now what am I going to do?"

"Put your wellies on instead," said Mum.

Grandad scowled.

"Ha-ha! Very funny," he said. "You're some help I must say!"

He sat down at the kitchen table.

Jamie and Fiona giggled into their cornflakes.

Dad poured some tea into Grandad's cup.

"Don't worry, Grandad," he said. "Benbow will find it."

Grandad scowled. "What, him? He's the stupidest dog in the world."

"He's very good at finding things," said Mum.

She gave Grandad a plate of bacon and eggs.

Jamie and Fiona began to shout, "Benbow! Benbow! Where are you?"

A big collie dog with muddy paws came running in from the garden.

Sheila Lavelle

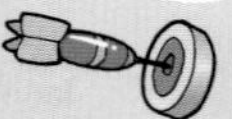

Comprehension

- To select accurate information to answer questions

Endings

Choose the right endings for these sentences:

1 When Grandad came downstairs he was very ______ { sad. / cross. / miserable. }

2 Grandad had lost a ______ { slipper. / shoe. / sock. }

3 Mum said he should put on his ______ { coat. / scarf. / wellies. }

4 Jamie and Fiona were eating ______ { bacon and eggs. / porridge. / cornflakes. }

5 Dad gave Grandad a ______ { glass of milk. / cup of coffee. / cup of tea. }

Finding out more

1 Why were Grandad's slippers so special to him?

2 What words are used to show how grumpy Grandad felt?

3 What type of dog was Benbow?

4 What did Grandad think about Benbow?

5 How do we know that the rest of the family thought Grandad was making too much fuss?

Helpful words

America collie
velvet giraffe
stupid normal
throat Betty world

Setting out a play

When a story is changed into a play it is set out in a different way.

Writing

- To change a story into a play script

Title	**Fetch the Slipper**
Characters	Grandad Mum Dad Jamie, aged about 9 Fiona, aged about 8 Benbow, the dog
Scene	*Early one morning. The family is having breakfast.*
Stage directions	*Grandad is coming down the stairs.*
GRANDAD	I've lost one of my slippers, one of my best velvet slippers, that Betty sent from America.
MUM	Put your wellies on instead.
GRANDAD (*scowling*)	Ha-ha! Very funny. You're some help I must say!

Grandad sits down with Jamie and Fiona who are giggling.
Dad pours Grandad a cup of tea.

DAD	Don't worry, Grandad, Benbow will find it.

Tip

Characters are the people in the play.

The **scene** is the setting of the play.

Stage directions tell the actors what to do.

Continue this play script using the text printed below.

Grandad scowled. "What, him? He's the stupidest dog in the world."
"He's very good at finding things," said Mum.
She gave Grandad a plate of bacon and eggs.
Jamie and Fiona began to shout, "Benbow! Benbow! Where are you?"
A big collie dog with muddy paws came running in from the garden.

Continuing the play

What might happen next?
The pictures will give you some ideas.

Continue your play in your book.
Try to finish with the slipper being found.

The Little Match-girl

It was snowing and the wind blew cold as darkness fell over the city. It was New Year's Eve. In the gathering gloom a little girl with bare feet padded quietly through the streets. She had been wearing her mother's slippers when she left home, but they were far too big, and she had lost them while hurrying quickly across the busy road. One of them was nowhere to be found, and a little boy unkindly had run off with the other. So now her bare feet were mottled blue and red with bitter cold.

In her old apron the little girl carried bundles of matches which her father had sent her out to sell, but nobody had bought a single match from her all day. Cold and hungry, she wearily wandered through the city.

After many hours the little girl crouched down in a corner between two houses. She shakily drew her knees up to her chest, but it seemed to make her even colder. She so much wanted to go home, but she was too afraid, for she had sold nothing the whole day. What would her father say?

Hans Christian Andersen (adapted from a translation by Richard Bamberger)

About the match-girl

Use words or phrases to complete these sentences:

1 *When she left home the match-girl was wearing ______ on her feet.*

2 *She had lost one slipper when she crossed a busy street and the other ______*

3 *In her apron she carried ______ which her father had sent her out to sell.*

4 *Between two houses the little girl crouched down and ______*

Comprehension

- To find detail about a character in a text

Helpful words

slippers matches knees bundles chest

Finding words

Find the words or phrases in the text to answer these questions:

1 How does the author describe the weather?

2 What words does the author use to tell us what time of day it is?

3 How does the author describe the match-girl's cold feet?

4 How did she feel when she made her weary way through the city streets?

Writing

- To write detailed character descriptions

Helpful words

Appearance
tall, thin boy
scowling face
mean eyes

Behaviour
swaggered down the street
pushed a small child over
ran off laughing
spiteful
nasty

Feelings
lonely
miserable that nobody wants him as a friend

Spiteful Sid

The story on page 16 tells us what the **character** of the match-girl was like.

It tells us

- **her appearance** (what she looked like)
  a little girl
  her bare feet were mottled blue and red
  carried matches in her old apron
- **her behaviour** (how she behaved)
  made her weary way through the streets
  crouched down
  drew her knees up to her chest
- **her feelings** (how she felt)
  cold
  weary
  hungry
  afraid

Now write some sentences to describe this character.
Your description should include:

- his appearance
- how you think he behaves
- the feelings he might have.

A character you know

Write a description of someone in your family.

Include information about his or her:

- appearance
- behaviour
- feelings about things.

Make your description interesting, by including some funny or unusual details.

What you do

1. Cut a hole in the lid of the container just big enough for the tubing to pass through.
2. Fix the balloon to one end of the tubing. Use the rubber band to hold it firmly in place.
3. Pass the tube through the hole in the lid, so that the balloon finishes on the underside of the lid.
4. Cut a hole near the bottom of the plastic container.
5. Screw the lid on to the container, with the end of the tube and the balloon inside.

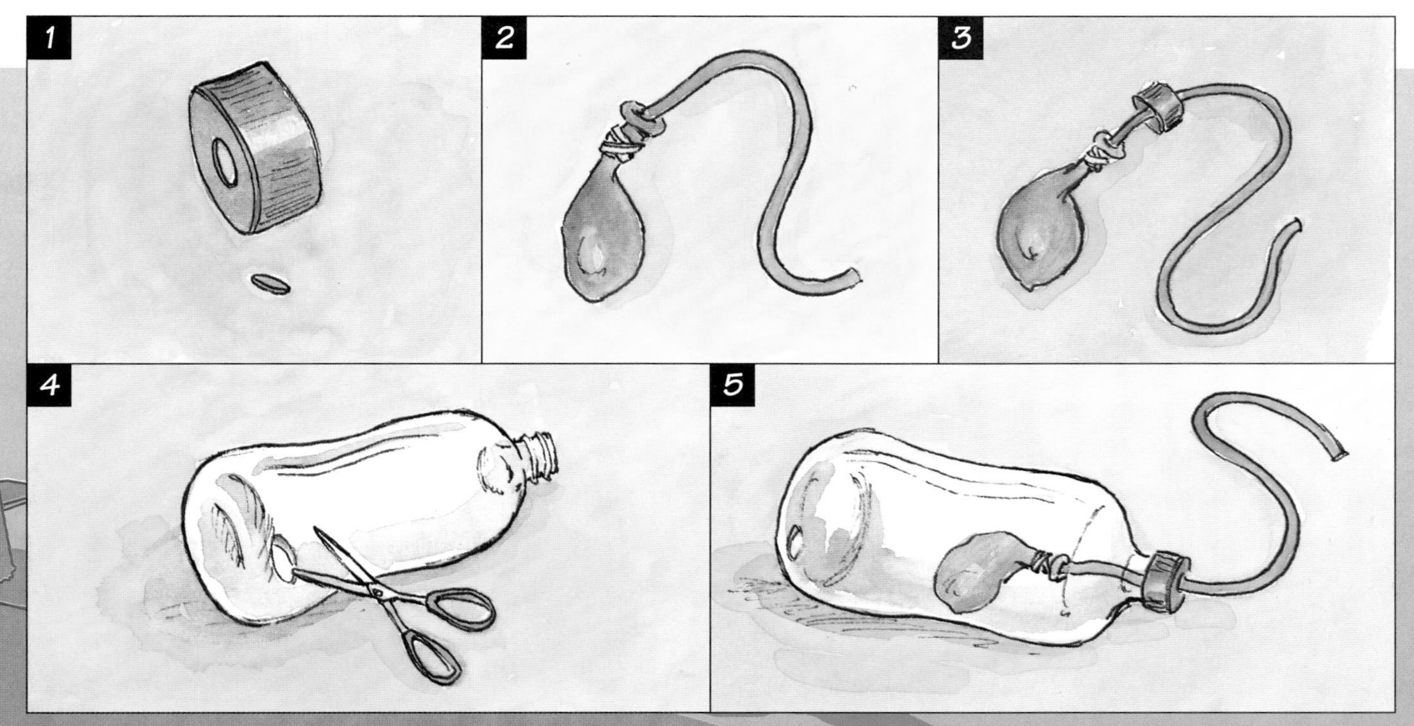

How to adjust your submarine

Try out your submarine in a sink or aquarium.

If the submarine won't sink when the container is filled with water, put a few pebbles inside it until it does.

Blow down the tube to see your submarine rise out of the water.

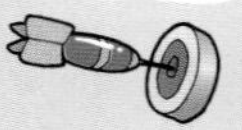

Comprehension

- To understand instructions

Helpful words

tightly tubing
elastic pebbles

Find out about making a submarine

1 What does the plastic container need to have?

2 How long does the plastic tubing need to be?

3 How big does the hole in the container need to be?

4 How do you fix the balloon to the rubber tubing?

5 If your submarine won't sink, what else do you need?

Submerged sentences

These sentences have lost some of their key words.

Find the correct words to make them complete and write the sentences in the correct order.

Pass the tube through ____________
____________ to one end of the tubing.

Cut a hole ____________ of the plastic container.

Screw ____________ onto the container.

____________ in the lid of the container.

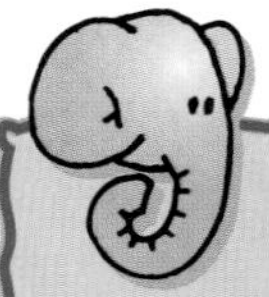

Remember

You need to number the instructions when you have put them in the correct order.

Making a sailing boat

Writing

- To write clear instructions

Choose *one* of these boats and write some instructions to show how to make it.

Set it out like this:

Title

What you need

-
-

What you do

1

2

Helpful words

wood pencil
string material
paper plastic
container lolly sticks
box cardboard
plastic bottle
elastic mast
sail cut
fix glue
tie paint

Tip

You can use diagrams to make the instructions clearer.

Decorating your boat

Use the layout above and write some instructions to show your reader how model boats can be decorated.

Charlie and the Chocolate Factory

Mr Wonka is proudly showing Charlie and the other visitors his secret inventing room.

Charlie Bucket stared around the gigantic room in which he now found himself. The place was like a witch's kitchen! All about him black metal pots were boiling and bubbling on huge stoves, and kettles were hissing and pans were sizzling, and strange iron machines were clanking and spluttering, and there were pipes running all over the ceiling and walls, and the whole place was filled with smoke and steam and delicious rich smells.

Mr Wonka himself had suddenly become even more excited than usual, and anyone could see that this was the room he loved best of all. He was hopping about among the saucepans and the machines like a child among his Christmas presents, not knowing which thing to look at first.

Roald Dahl

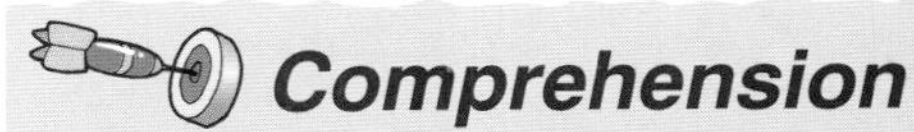

What Charlie saw

Write a sentence to answer each question:

1 Which room is Mr Wonka showing to the visitors?

2 What were the pots doing?

3 What were the kettles doing?

4 What were 'clanking and spluttering'?

5 What was 'running all over the ceiling and walls'?

6 Why did Mr Wonka become so excited when he went into the inventing room?

Comprehension

- To look in detail at a setting

Helpful words

pipes boiling
secret inventing room
clanking hissing
bubbling spluttering
loved best of all

Mr Wonka's inventing room

Which word or words have been used to describe these objects?

1 the pots *black, metal*

2 the room

3 the stoves

4 the machines

5 the smells

Remember

Words that describe people, places or things are called **adjectives**.

Writing

- To create an imaginative setting

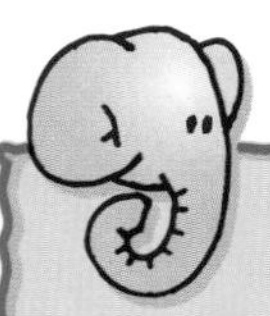

Remember

A **verb** tells us what actions were happening.

Setting the scene

To help us imagine the setting of this part of *Charlie and the Chocolate Factory*, the author has carefully and cleverly used

- **adjectives** huge, gigantic
- **verbs** hissing, spluttering

Imagine that you have gone into this room in the factory.

Write about the setting.

Think about the adjectives and verbs you could use.

Helpful words

crashing crunching
thunderous roaring
fascinating deafening

Remember

Write in sentences, using capital letters and full stops where they are needed.

Making a picture with words

In the passage the author, Roald Dahl, says that:

'The place was like a witch's kitchen!'
Mr Wonka was 'like a child among his Christmas presents'.

Remember

A **simile** is when we say something is **like** something else.

Think of some phrases to finish these similes.

1 The toffee machine sounded like ________
2 The sticks of rock rolled over like ________
3 The room looked like ________
4 The deafening noise in the room was like ________

Keeping a Hamster

Posters are a good way of showing information that you have collected. Tim found his information by:

Here is Tim's poster about looking after hamsters.

KEEPING HAMSTERS

Make sure your pet has a big cage, with interesting things for it to do.

It needs something hard to gnaw.

Make sure the cage is kept clean.

The hamster must have fresh, clean water at all times.

Don't feed it too much fruit or greens, or your hamster will become ill.

Always handle your pet very gently.

You are like a giant to a hamster!

YOUR HAMSTER DEPENDS ON YOU!

A hamster in a cage can't get its own food and water.

Looking after hamsters

Look back at Tim's poster to help you answer these questions.

Write your answers in sentences.

Sometimes there is more than one answer.

1. Where did Tim find out about hamsters?
2. What must a hamster always have in its cage?
3. How can you look after your hamster in the best way possible?
4. What food might make your hamster ill?

Understanding hamsters

Write a sentence to answer these questions.

1. Why does a hamster need a big cage?
2. Why does a hamster need something hard to gnaw?
3. Why should the hamster's cage be kept clean?
4. What do you think are the most important things to think about before you decide to keep a hamster?

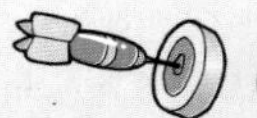

Comprehension

- To find information from a poster

Helpful words

provide a large cage
fruit and greens
interesting things to do
looking at books in a library
talking to people in a petshop
keep the cage clean
fresh water
working on a computer

Helpful words

exercise teeth
growing healthy
time illness
germs space

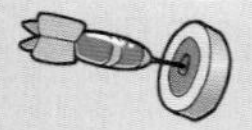

Writing

- To reseach information in order to write an article

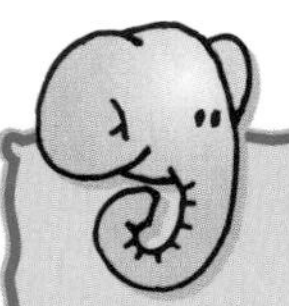

Remember

An article is written using sentences that start with a capital letter and end with a full stop.

The school magazine

Tim has been asked to write a short article for the school magazine about keeping hamsters.

He decides to find out some more information from an encyclopedia, and he makes a few notes about what he has read.

He can also use the information he found out for his poster.

Write the article for Tim. Before you begin, think how you will make an interesting opening paragraph, and then what you will say in each of the other sections of your article.

Tip

Your paragraphs might be:

1. Where hamsters first came from and why they make good pets.
2. How to keep a hamster healthy.
3. What the owner needs to think about before buying a hamster.

Collecting information

Tim wanted to find out more about the pets that the children in his class keep, and what they think about them. He decided to make a form with some questions for all the children to answer.

Write four questions that Tim might have asked.

The first one has been done for you.

Remember

Put a question mark at the end of each question.

Tip

A series of questions about the same subject is called a **questionnaire**.

1 What kind of pet do you have?
Tick the correct box.

dog	cat	fish	hamster
☐	☐	☐	☐
budgie	**rabbit**	**other**	**none**
☐	☐	☐	☐

The Space Journey

This is part of a first draft of a story about James and his space adventure. The author is not happy with it and wants to make some changes.

James leant forward along the branch. James was very careful. James was watching a strange creature. The creature was eating some leaves at the top of the tree and then it looked around, but did not spot him.

James moved but James had not noticed his torch was falling out of his pocket. James moved again, trying to hide behind a trunk, and suddenly a thump sounded through the forest. The torch had fallen to the ground.

James sat very still ... and slowly the creature turned.

*The author has now made some changes to improve it. This is called **editing**. Try to spot the changes.*

James carefully leant forward along the branch. He was watching an animal, or at least he thought it was an animal! The peculiar creature was browsing some succulent leaves at the top of the tree. It looked around, but did not spot him.

Terrified, James gently and slowly started to shift his position, but he hadn't noticed his torch slipping from his pocket. He moved again, struggling to get out of view of the creature, when suddenly a thump echoed through the silent forest. The torch had fallen to the ground.

James froze, but slowly, very slowly, the creature turned.

Comprehension

- To think about the order and detail of events

Sequencing the story

Write these sentences in the correct order.

The torch had fallen to the ground.

The peculiar creature was browsing some succulent leaves at the top of the tree.

A thump sounded through the forest.

James moved to get a better view.

James leant forward along the branch.

James and the creature

1 Why was James being very quiet?

2 Write 'browsing some succulent leaves' in your own words.

3 How do you think James felt as he watched the creature?

4 What do you think the creature will do next?

Helpful words

discovered noticed interested curious frightened escape chase scared tasty

Writing

- To edit and improve a passage of writing

Editing

This is the next part of the story but it has not been edited. Some changes need to be made. The words that need editing are underlined to help you. Add some interesting and descriptive words to make it more exciting.

Write the new version in your book.

James climbed down the tree. <u>James</u> grabbed his knife and <u>James</u> ran as <u>fast</u> as he could to the spaceship. <u>James</u> could hear the footsteps of the creature getting closer. <u>The creature was getting closer</u>. <u>James</u> pulled at the door handle.

James reaches safety

Edit the next part of the story. Then write a final paragraph.

The door would not open. James reached into his rucksack and pulled out a key. He pulled out the key and put it in the lock. James turned the key in the lock and the door swung open and James stepped inside to safety, or had he?

Whales

We can use different types of books to find information about whales.

- *From a dictionary:*

wet	*adj.* soaked in liquid, not dry
whale	*n.* the largest sea animal. It looks like a fish.
wharf	*n.* a landing stage to which ships can be moored

- *From an encyclopedia:*

Whales

There are nearly eighty types of whale. Some, like the dolphin and porpoise, are quite small, but the blue whale is the largest animal in the world. It weighs more than 100 tonnes – as much as about twenty elephants, or all the people in a small town of about 2000. It is even bigger than the biggest dinosaur. Not even the giant brontosaurus was as large.

Whales are not fish. They are mammals like cows, lions, or humans. Like all mammals, they breathe air, have warm blood, have some hair on their bodies, have babies rather than lay eggs, and feed milk to their young.

- *From an information book:*

What a meal!

A huge creature like a blue whale needs large amounts of food. Most of the bigger whales don't have teeth but filters, called baleen plates, for catching tiny sea creatures, especially krill. A blue whale will eat about 4 tonnes of krill a day, which is about the weight of 14,000 potatoes!

Comprehension

- To find key words in a text

Remember

Each of these sentences begins with a **capital letter** and ends with a **full stop**.

Helpful words

swim resemble
encyclopedia
dictionary weigh
heavy information

All about whales

Write only the facts that are true:

- There are over ninety types of whale.
- Dolphins and porpoises are small whales.
- Whales are big fish.
- Whales are mammals.
- Whales feed milk to their young.
- Bigger whales do not have teeth but filters, called baleen plates.

More about whales

Write a sentence to answer these questions:

1 Name the different sources that have been used to find information about whales.

2 Were any dinosaurs as big as blue whales?

3 Which words come before and after the whale in this dictionary?

4 Why do some people think whales are fish?

5 Why has the illustrator drawn a picture of a blue whale on top of a herd of elephants?

Blue whales

Write five facts about whales.

Use the information from the sources on page 37.

The first one has been done for you.

- *A blue whale is the largest animal in the world.*

If you can, add some more facts of your own.

Writing

- To select information to make a wallchart

Tip

Pictures and labelled diagrams are a good way of displaying information simply.

Making a wallchart

Make a wallchart about blue whales for a younger child.

Make the information very clear and make your wallchart interesting and eye-catching.

Include at least five facts about whales in your wallchart.

The Lion, the Witch and the Wardrobe

These two extracts describe the scene as winter changes to spring.

Every moment the patches of green grew bigger and the patches of snow grew smaller. Every moment more and more of the trees shook off their robes of snow. Soon, wherever you looked, instead of white shapes you saw the dark green of firs or the black prickly branches of bare oaks and beeches and elms. Then the mist turned from white to gold and presently cleared away altogether. Shafts of delicious sunlight struck down on to the forest floor and overhead you could see a blue sky between the tree tops … .

There was no trace of the fog now. The sky became bluer and bluer, and now there were white clouds hurrying across it from time to time. In the wide glades there were primroses. A light breeze sprang up which scattered drops of moisture from the swaying branches and carried cool, delicious scents against the faces of the travellers.

C. S. Lewis

Changes

These extracts are about changes. Choose an ending from the box to complete these sentences.

1 The patches of green grew bigger
2 Instead of white shapes
3 The mist
4 The sky became bluer and bluer,
5 A light breeze sprang up

turned from white to gold. which scattered drops of moisture from the swaying branches. and the patches of snow grew smaller. you saw the dark green of firs. and now there were white clouds hurrying across it.

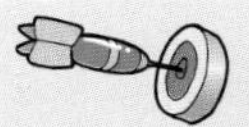

Comprehension

- To identify descriptive phrases

Looking at the description

When writing about a scene an author may ask the reader to think about some or all of their senses.

In this passage the author has mainly written about things that can be seen.

Make a list of six phrases from the extract that describe what can be seen. The first one is done for you.

patches of green grew bigger

Tip

The senses are seeing, hearing, touching, smelling and tasting.

Remember

A **phrase** is a group of words.

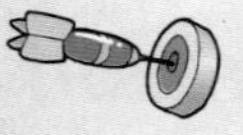

Writing

- To select and use good descriptive words and phrases

Moonlight in the harbour

Helpful words

reflections surface calm
still waves splashing
bobbing shapes
sheltered lapping
peaceful silent
quiet beautiful

1 Write some words or phrases, to describe **the sea**. The first is done for you.

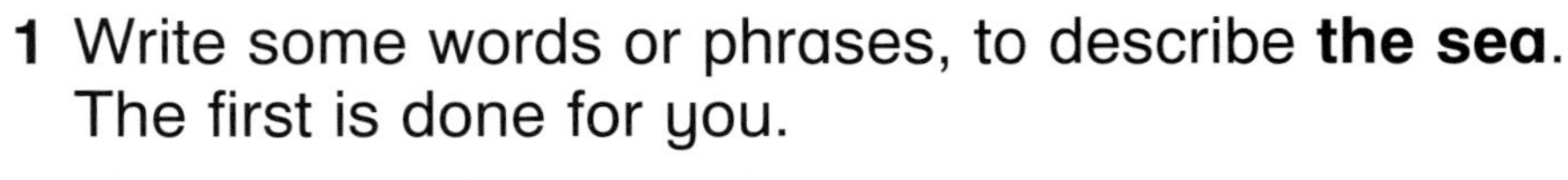

shining in the moonlight

2 Write some words or phrases, to describe **the boats**.

3 Write some words or phrases, to describe **the whole scene**.

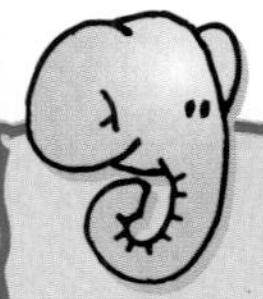

Remember

A good description means that someone else can imagine the scene without looking at the picture.

Setting the scene with a description

Write a description of the harbour scene.

Use some of the words and phrases you have already written to help you.

Patterns in poetry

Write these sentences, filling in the missing words:

1 This poem has _______ verses.

2 The _______, the _______ and the _______ verses are exactly the same.

3 The second and fourth verses are conversations between _______.

4 In the first verse there are _______ long lines followed by two _______ lines and one medium line.

5 In the second verse the conversation is between the _______ cow and the _______ _______.

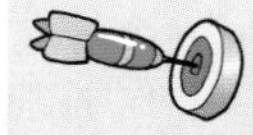

Comprehension

- To recognise some patterns in poetry

Tip

Verses that are repeated are sometimes called a **chorus**.

More patterns

Copy this table and fill in the information.

Verse	Number of lines	End words that rhyme
1	5	lay, May, away A-chewing, A-mooing
2		
3		
4		
5		

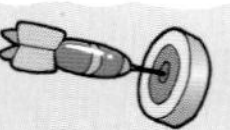

Writing

- To create a poem using a set structure

Helpful words

fight light sight might height night tight

Remember

The second and the fourth line should rhyme.

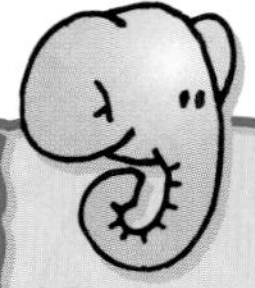

Remember

Use speech marks to indicate what is actually said.

Cow conversation

Write a sixth verse for this poem.
You will need to try out ideas on a piece of paper before you copy it into your book.
Make a list of four things that the cows might talk about.

farmers

____

____

____

Choose one of these for your verse.

Now fill in the gaps.

"____________," said the brown cow.

"____________," said the white.

____

____

Birds

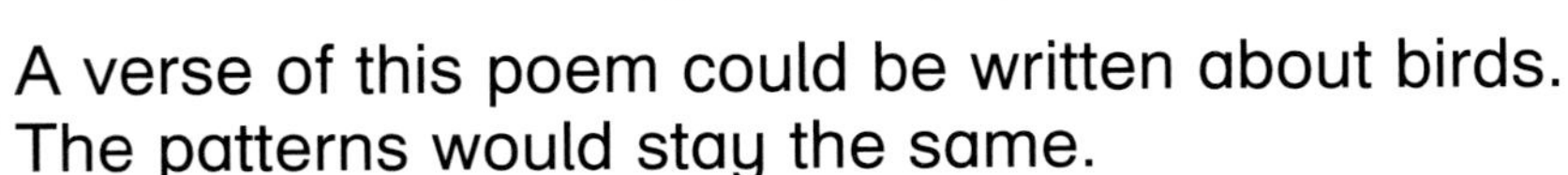

A verse of this poem could be written about birds.
The patterns would stay the same.
Put your own words in the gaps but make sure that the third and fourth lines rhyme.

Half the time they ____________ , and all the time they stay

Down in ____________ , the ____________ month of May.

A-____________,

A-____________,

To pass the hours away.

In the Playground

I saw a little girl I hate
And kicked her with my toes.
She turned
And smiled
And KISSED me!
Then she punched me in the nose.

Extract from 'A Rumbugdin' by Arnold Spilka

We can't possibly have rules for everything, and we shouldn't need rules to tell us not to kick or punch other people, but some rules are helpful.

Here are the rules in one school:

Do ...

Do place litter in the bins.

Do close the gate as soon as you come into school.

Do help new children to find friends.

Do think of others as much as yourself.

Don't ...

Don't play with balls near to windows.

Don't go out of the gate without permission.

Don't climb over walls or fences.

Don't run around in groups so that other children might be knocked over.

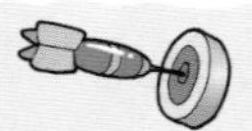

Comprehension

- To think about rules

Spot the mistakes

Ali has not copied the playground rules carefully.
Spot the mistakes he has made and write them correctly.

Do …	Don't …
Do place letters in the bins.	Don't play with marbles near to windows.
Do close the gate before you come into school.	Don't go out of the gate without pencils.
Do help new teachers to find new friends.	Do climb over walls or fences.

Helpful words

kissed punched
tidy clean
dangerous damage
everyone protect

Rules are for us

Write a sentence to answer each question:

1. What happened to the person who kicked the little girl?
2. Why don't we have a playground rule to say 'Don't kick other children'?
3. Why is there a school rule about litter?
4. Explain the reasons why there is a school rule about climbing on walls and fences.
5. Why do schools have rules?

Visiting the lock

Writing

- To write a list of rules

Ali's class is going to visit a nearby lock for the day. The lock-keeper is going to show them around and tell them about the lock.

The teacher wants to make sure the class have a happy, interesting day so she gives each person a list of things to do.

> *Take waterproof clothing.*
> *Be polite.*
> *Take food for the ducks and swans.*
> *Keep with your friend.*
> *Ask sensible questions.*
> *Take a packed lunch.*

Tip

Often rules are about safety.

Write the four **most important** rules in your book.

Use the title *Do ...*

How did you decide which ones to leave out? Write two sentences to explain your choice.

Rules for the day

Write four more rules starting with *Don't ...* that the teacher might write before the visit. Only write the most important ones.

Use the title *Don't ...*

Helpful words

water rubbish chatter swans nest

Hue Boy

Some of us are short, some are tall, some are fat and some are thin. Some people have curly hair, others straight. No two people are the same. It is good that we are all different. It would be a very boring world if we all looked the same. But sometimes some very unkind people tease others about how they look, and this can make them very unhappy. Hue Boy is feeling unhappy for this reason, because he is very short.

Then one morning, their neighbour Carlos said, "I know, Hue Boy. Some stretching exercises will do the trick. Ten minutes a day. That's all you need to do." …

At school his classmates chanted,
"Heels, heels, high heeled shoes,
Needed for the smallest boy in the school."
Hue Boy looked down.

But Miss Harper, the teacher, said, "Stuff and nonsense! Walk tall, Hue Boy. Hold your head up. That's all you need to do!"
Still Hue Boy didn't grow one little bit.
He still didn't grow at all, at all.

Next they visited Doctor Gamas. He examined Hue Boy thoroughly.

Then he said, "There is absolutely nothing wrong with you, Hue Boy. Some people are short and perfectly healthy, you know."

"Lawdy," cried Mum. "This problem seems to be bigger than this village!"

Rita Phillips Mitchell

Comprehension

- To understand different points of view in a story

Hue Boy's problem

Write and complete these sentences.

1 *Carlos advised Hue Boy* ________
2 *His classmates suggested he should wear* ________
3 *Miss Harper told him to* ________
4 *The doctor said that* ________
5 *Hue Boy's mum thought that the problem was* ________

Helpful words

exercises head high-heeled shoes wrong healthy bigger village stretching

Think for yourself

Write a sentence to answer these questions:

1 Why did Carlos advise him to exercise more?
2 How do you think Hue Boy felt when his classmates teased him?
3 Why do you think the teacher and the doctor were not worried about Hue Boy's height?
4 What would you say to Hue Boy about 'his problem' if you were his friend?

Helpful words

healthy grow unhappy miserable ignore forget worry

Writing

- To explore and solve problems in a story

Tip

It would be helpful to give names to the two children in the story.

Helpful words

trampoline playing
happy older
unfair pushed
sports hall attendant
asked finished

Trouble in the sports hall

Look at these pictures and use them to write a story.

In your **first paragraph** describe:
- the characters and what they are doing
- the setting.

In your **second paragraph** describe:
- the new characters, especially their appearance and behaviour.

In your **third paragraph** describe:
- what happens
- how the problem might be solved.

Solving problems

Often stories are about solving problems. Draw this table in your book and write a sentence to explain what you might do when these problems occur.

Problem	What I should do
I am being bullied in the playground.	
A stranger asks me to get in a car.	
I find a £10 note that has fallen out of an old lady's purse.	

The New Car Park

126, Cardiff Road
Swaddleton
CF16 9RF

12th November

Dear Mrs Barnard,

I am writing to complain that the council is going to make a car park on the piece of land where we play in the middle of our estate.

The grown-ups think it is a great idea because there aren't enough places for cars to park along the roads, but most of us children think it is a very bad idea.

We call it 'the Green'. It is the only place we have to play. I know it looks scruffy and muddy, but that is because we play on it so much the grass doesn't have much chance to grow. If we didn't have the Green we would have to play in the road and that would be dangerous. Is that what the council wants us to do?

I hope you can stop this plan. My friends and I will vote for you when we are older if you help us now!

Yours sincerely,

Jessica Lindsay

Comprehension

- To examine an issue

Helpful words

built parking
dangerous because
safely complain

Save our Green

Write a sentence to answer these questions:

1 Why did Jessica write to Mrs Barnard?

2 Why does 'the Green' look scruffy?

3 Why do some people want the car park?

4 Why does Jessica want to stop the car park being built?

5 What would happen to the children's games if the car park was built?

Slogans

1 A slogan is a short group of words to catch people's attention and put over a point of view.
Write four slogans that could be used by the children who were against the new car park.
The first one has been done for you.

- *Keep the Green for games.*
-
-
-

2 The adults have a different point of view.
Think of three slogans they could use to persuade people that the car park is a good idea.

- *Safer roads with the new car park.*
-
-

The new supermarket

A new supermarket is being planned but not everyone is happy about it.

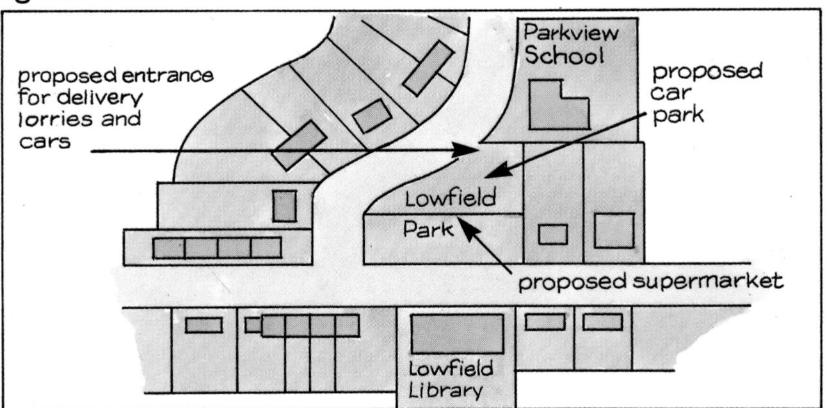

Look carefully at the map and think of the reasons for and against building the new supermarket. Copy this table and fill it in.

Reasons for the supermarket being built	Reasons against the supermarket being built
1	1

Letter to the council

Imagine you are a pupil at Parkview School. Write to Mrs Barnard of the Lowfield Council to try to persuade the council not to build the supermarket.

Parkview School
Brook Road
Lowfield
LF2 4TG

6th May

Dear Mrs Barnard,

(First explain why you are writing this letter.)

(Next give your reasons why you do not want the supermarket to be built.)

Yours sincerely,

Writing

- To examine different points of view and presenting ideas in a letter

Tip

Try to imagine what it would be like if you lived in this area.

Mary and Sarah

Mary likes smooth things,
Things that glide:
Sleek skis swishing down a mountainside.

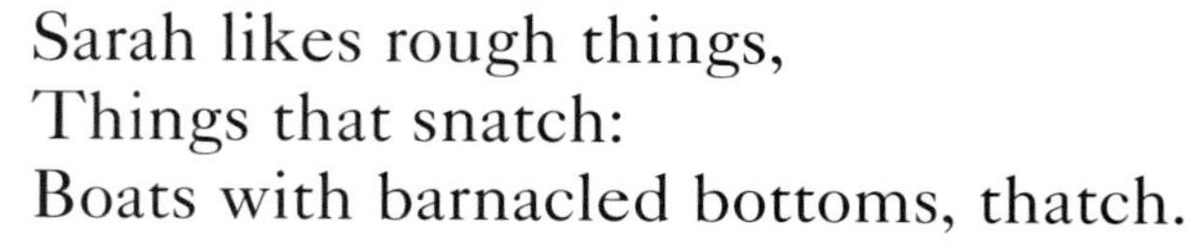

Sarah likes rough things,
Things that snatch:
Boats with barnacled bottoms, thatch.

Mary likes smooth things,
Things all mellow:
Milk, silk, runny honey, tunes on a cello.

Sarah likes rough things,
Things all troubly:
Crags, snags, bristles, thistles, fields left stubbly.

Mary says—polish,
Sarah says—rust,
Mary says—mayonnaise,
Sarah says—crust.

Sarah says—hedgehogs,
Mary says—seals,
Sarah says—sticklebacks,
Mary says—eels…

Mary and Sarah—
They'll never agree
Till peaches and coconuts
Grow on one tree.

Richard Edwards

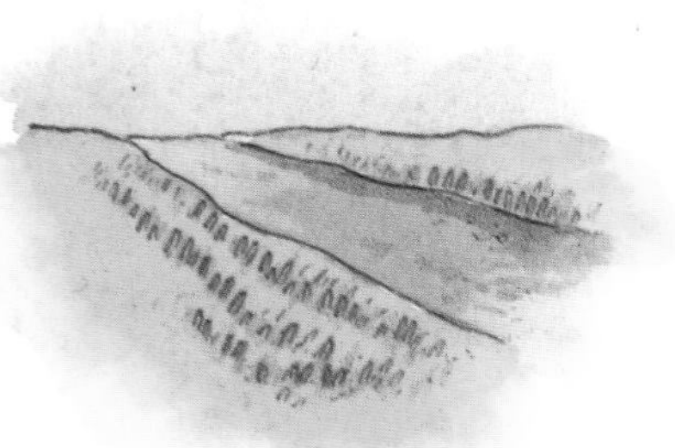

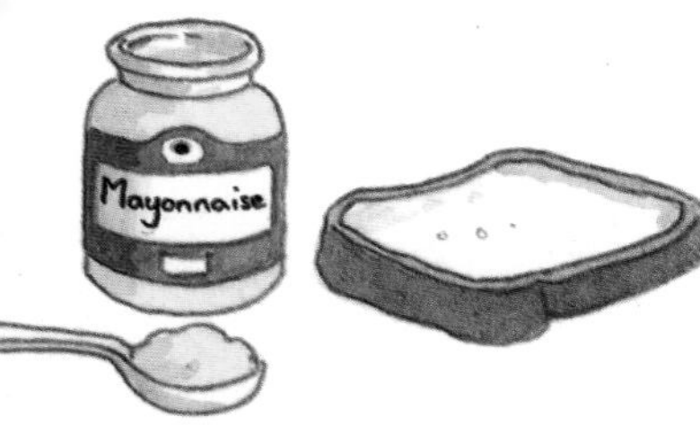

Comprehension

- To pick out details in a poem

Rough or smooth

Copy the table.
Sort these words and phrases into the right column.

runny honey fields left stubbly hedgehogs
milk, silk tunes on a cello eels
bristles, thistles boats with barnacled bottoms
sleek skis swishing down a mountainside

Mary likes smooth things	Sarah likes rough things

Favourite things

Write a sentence to answer these questions:

1. What is it about boats that Sarah likes?
2. What does it mean when the field is described as 'left stubbly'?
3. What kind of tunes would be played on the cello for Mary?
4. Why does Mary like eels?
5. How does the poet tell us that Mary and Sarah will never agree?

Helpful words

peaches barnacles
stalks slippery
quiet gentle
coconuts impossible

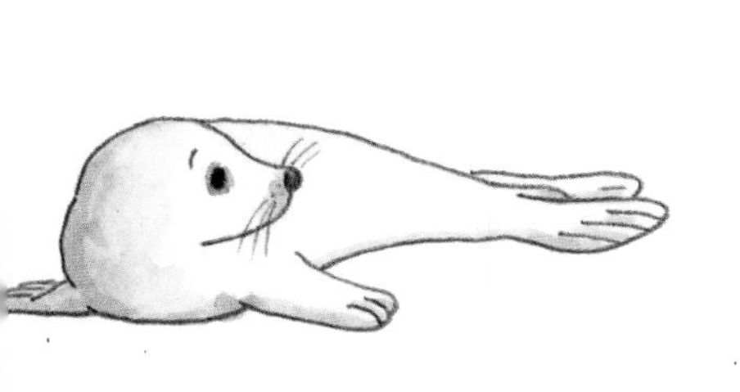

Writing

- To create a poem using a set structure

Helpful words

slow blow
glow know
row show
flow tow

Helpful words

not pot spot
forgot knot
lot parrot

Green or yellow?

Write a poem yourself about two people who like different colours.

First, copy the table and collect words and phrases that you might use.

Some have been done to get you started.

Green things	Yellow things
juicy green apples, leaves	blazing sunshine bananas

Set your poem out like this:

John likes green things
Things that grow:

____

Jane likes yellow things
Things that are hot:

____

Remember

The second and fourth lines should rhyme.

What do they say?

Fill in the gaps with suitable words that rhyme.

Jane says — butter,
John says — __________
Jane says — yellow lines,
John says — __________

Now write out your poem in your best handwriting and draw pictures around it.

Badgers

Look at these photographs of badgers.

A secret life

Badgers are well known and liked, but few people have seen one. They are nocturnal creatures, like owls and bats, coming out only at night. They have short, strong legs with large claws. This means they can dig burrows very quickly. They are also strong, fierce fighters. They eat mice, squirrels and other small animals, as well as some plants.

The 'badger problem'

Some farmers think that badgers carry TB, an illness that they pass on to cows. TB is such a serious illness that if only one cow on a farm has it, none of the milk on the farm can be sold.

But no one has proved whether badgers really give cows TB, it is only one possible cause. To try to discover the truth it has been suggested that all the badgers in some areas should be killed, to see whether cows no longer catch TB.

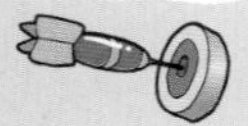

Comprehension

- To decide what can be found out from a passage

Tip

You need to think carefully about some of these answers.

Helpful words

burrows squirrels
bat illness killed
night-time serious owl

True, false or can't tell

Copy these sentences.
Write *true*, *false* or *can't tell* next to each one.

1. *Most people have seen a badger.*
2. *Badgers come out at night.*
3. *Badgers pass on TB to cows.*
4. *Farmers think that badgers carry an illness that they pass on to sheep.*
5. *Badgers are fierce fighters.*
6. *If one cow on a farm has TB none of the milk can be sold.*

Thinking about badgers

Write a sentence to answer these questions:

1. What does 'nocturnal' mean?
2. Name two creatures that are nocturnal.
3. What problems would a badger have if it damaged its claws?
4. Why don't squirrels think of badgers as their friends?
5. What is the 'badger problem'?
6. Do you think the suggestion for solving the 'badger problem' is a good one? Give your reasons.

Summaries

1 Read again the paragraph on page 61 called **A secret life**.

It tells us about **what badgers are like** and **what they eat**.

In your own words, write two sentences about a badger's life.

2 Write a summary of **The 'badger problem'**. Write two sentences about the most important points.

Writing

- To write a summary

Remember

A summary is a shortened version. You need only include the most important points.

Badgers and their young

Badgers live in a sett which is a long series of tunnels underground. These tunnels have been dug over many years by members of the same family. Each sett has several different entrances and a number of nest chambers or sleeping chambers. Sleeping chambers are usually lined with grass and leaves but other strange items have been found. In one sett 250 golf balls were found!

It is in the nest chambers, in late January or early February, that most of the young are born. When they are first born they are pink with grey silky fur. Their eyes open at five weeks but they stay underground for the first eight weeks. Gradually the cubs become more confident and follow their mothers above ground but they are quick to return underground if danger threatens.

Write a summary of **Badgers and their young**. Make sure you include all the most important facts. You must not use more than sixty words.

Jack and the Meanstalk

Professor Jack had been experimenting to find ways to make plants grow bigger and faster …

Early next morning, Professor Jack heard a loud crash. His experiment had worked so well that one of the plants had gone right through the roof.

The villagers, the fire brigade, and two television crews all arrived to see the amazing plant.

The plant went on growing and growing. It soared high up into the sky, until it was almost out of sight.

The plant grew so high that it burst through the ozone layer, and its thousands of leaves blocked out the sunlight. Fighter planes tried to shoot it down, but still it grew.

Brian and Rebecca Wildsmith

- To compare stories

Comparing stories

Jack and the Meanstalk is a different account of a traditional story.

Draw this table and fill it in to show the way the story has changed.

Old title-Jack and the Beanstalk	New title-Jack and the Meanstalk
The story is about a young boy called Jack.	
Villagers came to see the enormous plant.	
The plant grew up into the clouds.	
The beanstalk stopped growing and Jack climbed up it.	
Jack chopped it down with an axe.	

The plant gets bigger

Write a sentence to answer these questions:

1 What woke Professor Jack the morning after he had started the experiment?

2 Do you think he was pleased that his experiment worked so well?

3 Write the headline that could have been in the newspaper the next day.

4 How do you think the people felt when the plant went through the ozone layer?

5 Why was it important for the fighter planes to try to stop the plant growing?

Helpful words

blocked crash
standing enormous
growing scared
amazed alarmed
fighter ozone
scientist

Writing

- To write a different ending

What happens next?

Who can save the planet?

Decide who is going to resolve the problem.
Write some sentences to describe your character.
Say how Professor Jack meets him or her.

The planet is saved

Your character needs to come up with a clever, and perhaps unusual, idea to kill the giant plant.

Write the ending to the story.
Think about:

- how they work out a plan to resolve the problem
- what others think of the plan
- how they feel before and after the plant dies
- what happens to them in the end.

Helpful words

poison shrivelled
slowly gradually
rustling calm
magic ingenious
chopped crashed
thunderous noise
dangerous quickly
peaceful

Opening Soon!

Comprehension

- To decide between fact and opinion

Helpful words

trampolining half-price
bowling membership
cafe friendly
swimming perfect
burger

Looking at posters

Some answers need to be in sentences and others can be a few words.

1. What is opening soon?
2. What special offer is used to encourage you to join quickly?
3. Name three different sports you can do at the new sports centre.
4. What else can you do at the sports centre?
5. What do you think this poster wants you to think about the new sports centre?

Fact or opinion

This poster is a mixture of fact and opinion.

Copy these statements and underline the part that is opinion.

The first one is done for you.

- 2 Luxury Swimming Pools
- Magnificent Sports Hall
- Terrific Trampolines
- Brilliant Bowling Alley
- Cafe/Burger Bar – for perfect parties!
- Friendly, helpful instructors
- A perfect place to meet your friends for FUN! FUN! FUN!

Summer fair

There is going to be a summer fair at a local school and there will be many different stalls.
You have been asked to design a poster to encourage people to come.
Before you start, make a table like this to help you collect the facts together.

Title of the event	
Where it is to be held	
Date and time it opens	
List of the stalls and other attractions	
Refreshments that are provided	

Now make a list of about six words or phrases that might make people want to come to the fair.

- *fantastic family fun*
-
-
-
-
-

Homemade Cakes

Making a poster

Use a whole page in your book or a piece of paper to make your poster.

Position your writing carefully. Think about the part of the poster that you want to make the most important.

When decorating your poster make sure all the writing is still clear.

Writing

- To plan a poster for the greatest impact

Tip

Alliteration (starting each word with the same letter) can add impact.

Tip

Write lightly in pencil until you are sure you have the writing in the right place.

Camel Wrestling

Bad-tempered camels

Camels look elegant and graceful, but they can be bad-tempered, irritable animals! (We sometimes say that someone has "got the hump" when we mean that they are in a bad mood.)

In the wild, camels are naturally fierce. The males often attack other male camels, sometimes hurting each other with their sharp teeth. Like most people, camels don't seem to like the winter very much. They get more irritable than usual in the cold weather, and even more aggressive!

In Roman times

The Romans used to organise camel-wrestling competitions. Camels were valuable and no owner would want serious harm to come to them, so the animals wore muzzles to protect their opponents from injury. The camels would enter the arena from opposite ends and fight by pushing and shoving each other. In the end the weaker one usually gave in, falling to the ground or running out of the arena.

The Romans thought camel wrestling was great fun!

Find out about camels

Write some sentences to answer these questions:

1 Why were camels used for fighting?

2 What did the wild camels use to attack other camels?

3 Why did the camels wear muzzles when they were wrestling?

4 Why did the owners of the camels want no harm to come to them?

5 How did camels fight?

6 Do you think camel wrestling was cruel?

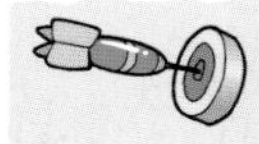

Comprehension

- To think carefully about information in a text and some common sayings

Remember

Each sentence must begin with a capital letter and end with a full stop.

Helpful words

injury fierce
teeth pushing
valuable protect
aggressive shoving

Playing with words

These phrases sound a little odd.

Explain what each one means.

The first one has a picture to help you.

1 He's got the hump!

2 He's over the moon.

3 She's got square eyes.

4 Don't let the cat out of the bag.

5 They managed to catch the bus.

Writing

- To express a point of view

Animals and sports

Make a table of animal sports like this:

Horses	horse racing show jumping fox hunting
Dogs	
Birds	
Fish	

Add as many other types of animal sports as you can.

What do you think

Some people think it is cruel for animals to be used in sports, but others think that the animals enjoy it.

What do you think?

Copy and finish these sentences.

Write some more sentences as well, if you wish.

I think that sports involving animals are __________

I have several reasons for thinking this. My first reason is __________

Another important reason is __________

Therefore, although some people think __________*, I think* __________

Tip

Before you begin, write a list of all your reasons. Then sort them into order, with the most important ones first.